MONSTER SPELLER

STORY BY **ROBERT MARSH**

ILLUSTRATED BY **TOM PERCIVAL**

raintree 🍃

...ne company — publishers for children

Raintree is an imprint of Capstone Global Library Limited, a company incorporated in England and Wales having its registered office at 264 Banbury Road, Oxford, OX2 7DY – Registered company number: 6695582

www.raintree.co.uk
myorders@raintree.co.uk

Creative Director: Heather Kindseth
Designer: Brann Garvey
Production by Tori Abraham
Printed and bound in China

ISBN 978 1 4747 8442 9

British Library Cataloguing in Publication Data
A full catalogue record for this book is available from the British Library.

STARRING...

DWIGHT

GABBY

HEADMASTER
BURNS

MR PINE

8

It's okay, Ms Barkley. You can come down.

Dwight won't hurt you.

16

19

24

33

HOW TO DRAW GABBY

1. Did you know drawings of people start with shapes? For Gabby, draw a circle for a head. Add two short lines for a neck and a slender rectangle for the body.

2. Next, draw Gabby's hair around the circle and across the forehead. Add simple shapes to map out where her arm and legs are going to be.

3. Now it's time to add her hands and facial features. Rub out lines you no longer need.

4. Now add details like clothing, hat, shoes and a hair clip. Give her an upper lip, eyelashes and fingers.

5. Make sure you rub out all the extra lines that you no longer need. This will clean up your drawing.

6. It's time to colour. What kind of jumper will Gabby wear? What colour are her shoes? It is your choice!

AUTHOR

Robert Marsh grew up in Omaha, Nebraska, USA, but longed to live somewhere else. He pretended not to live in Omaha by reading lots of books. Every week, Marsh checked out 20 books from the library. As he didn't have time to read all of those books, he would read the first chapter of each and make up the rest of the story. Marsh now makes up stories for a living and doesn't live in Omaha. Dreams do come true.

ILLUSTRATOR

Tom Percival grew up in Shropshire, a place of such remarkable beauty that he decided to sit in his room every day, drawing pictures and writing stories. But that was a long time ago, and much has changed since then. Now, Percival lives in Bristol, where he sits in his room all day, drawing pictures and writing stories. His patient girlfriend, Liz, and their baby son, Ethan, keep him company.

GLOSSARY

ashamed feeling embarrassed or guilty

blackmail a threat to reveal a secret about someone unless the person grants a favour or pays money

dictionaries books that list words in a language in alphabetical order and explains what they mean

district-wide throughout a certain area

interpret to translate for people who speak different languages

jicama edible part of the yam bean, used in Mexican cooking

reggae a type of rhythmic popular music from the West Indies

speech therapy a treatment to help people speak more clearly

volunteers people who offer to do a job for free

werewolves people who can change into wolves

DISCUSSION QUESTIONS

1. Why didn't Headmaster Burns want Dwight to compete in the spelling bee? Do you think he had a good reason?

2. To prepare Dwight for the spelling bee, Gabby helps him practise spelling words. Have you ever practised for a certain event? What did you do?

3. Mr Pine did not want anyone to know about his love for Fluffy Bunnies. What do you think would have happened if the secret got out?

WRITING PROMPTS

1. How would you change the ending of this book? Write a new ending.

2. Create an advert for Ultra-Fluffy Super Bunnies, Mr Pine's favourite stuffed animals. Make sure you include a catchy slogan.

3. Write a news article to go with one of the headlines shown on page 33. Include quotes from the people who were there.